ALBERT H. MUNSELL

A COLOR NOTATION

BY

A. H. MUNSELL

AN ILLUSTRATED SYSTEM DEFINING ALL COLORS AND
THEIR RELATIONS BY MEASURED
SCALES OF

Hue, Value, and Chroma

INTRODUCTION BY ROYAL B. FARNUM

Twelfth Edition
(edited and rearranged)

MUNSELL COLOR COMPANY, INC.

BALTIMORE, MD., 21218
1975

PREFACE

IN EDITING this revision of "A Color Notation" it is quite appropriate to give a brief outline of the life of its author. Albert H. Munsell was born in Boston, Massachusetts, in 1858. He grew up with a great interest in out-of-door sports, but most of all he loved to spend his time on the ships and tugs on the water front. His love for the sea greatly influenced his paintings in later life. His artistic ability and subtle sense of color began to assert itself when he was quite young, and upon his graduation from high school he entered the Massachusetts Normal Art School.

It is of interest to note that during his student days his mind was already turning toward color problems. In 1879 he read Professor Rood's "Modern Chromatics" and followed the suggestion contained therein by placing two pyramids base to base, painting them white at the top, and black at the bottom, with the spectral colors arranged in a band around the faces of the pyramids.

Upon graduating, he was awarded a fellowship for foreign study. In Paris he attended Julien Academy where his creditable work enabled him to take the examinations for the Beaux Arts. At the end of his first year he won second prize in their yearly competition. His painting, "The Ascension of Elijah," still hangs in the galleries of the Beaux Arts. Later he won the highly prized Catherine de' Medici scholarship which gave him an extra year's study in Rome.

[3]

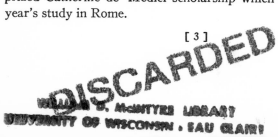

A COLOR NOTATION

When he returned to America he was appointed lecturer in color composition and artistic anatomy at the Normal Art School in Boston, a position which he held until 1915.

During his vacation in the summer of 1898, the thought occurred to him that it might be helpful in teaching his class in color composition, if he were able to describe the colors on his sketches in definite terms. He therefore arranged these colors on a circle, then on a sphere. From this small beginning was developed the Munsell Color System.

In 1900 Mr. Munsell experimented freely with various forms of color charts, and perfected the use of Maxwell discs as a means of color matching. In 1905 he published the first edition of "A Color Notation." This was followed by the production of his first color chart and a simple set of school supplies made according to his system.

During the next ten years he produced singly the several Munsell Color Charts, which he later assembled into the "Munsell Color Atlas."

Mr. Munsell was frequently called upon to lecture on his system in this country and in 1914 he addressed audiences in London, Paris, and Berlin. His lectures abroad overtaxed his strength, with the result that he returned to this country practically an invalid. Although he was still able to keep in close touch with the development of his system, his health failed steadily.

Early in 1918, with the cooperation of a number of his friends, the Munsell Color Company was formed. He hoped that this company might develop actively the accuracy and applicability of his system. Although the death of Mr. Munsell came later in the same year before he was able to reach his ultimate goal, the company he organized still carries on the work he started.

PREFACE

Mr. Munsell had in mind a revision of "A Color Notation." A careful study of his published works and unpublished notes has enabled the editors to present the three dimensions of color in a manner consistent with his later ideas. Except for the addition of an occasional word or sentence, the main text of this revision is entirely Mr. Munsell's work.

We wish to express our appreciation to Messrs. Royal B. Farnum, Blanchard Brown, Arthur S. Allen, Milton E. Bond, Sidney M. Newhall, and the Misses Dorothy Nickerson and Harriet J. Taylor for their encouragement and advice, and to Messrs. Deane B. Judd, Kenneth L. Kelly, William Beck, and Miss Lorain Fawcett for their contributions to the notes in Appendix B. We are also indebted to the Strathmore Paper Company for permission to use certain text written by Mr. A. H. Munsell for their publication "A Grammar of Color."

A. E. O. MUNSELL

INTRODUCTION

COLOR phenomena have been defined by many scientists and taught by many teachers. Numerous books have been published treating of its physical and its psychological aspects. Artists and designers have for centuries combined colors for decorative and pictorial purposes. Nature constantly envelopes us in a world of color. Man surrounds himself with it as a natural impulse. And yet to the average man and woman it has remained something of a mystery, an expression of Nature taken for granted but not fully understood.

Many attempts have been made to describe color but none until now have been altogether satisfactory. Trade names are as non-descript as they are absurd; scientific explanations are unintelligible to the layman; the artist's vocabulary is likewise limited to his profession. Some means of noting colors, exactly defining their characteristics or attributes, just as sounds are written on music scores, would not only be practical but would serve to bring these elusive but common phenomena within the comprehension and daily use of all mankind. The task would seem to be impossible, but "A Color Notation" not only does this, it presents the whole question of color in a simple, logical manner which, if carefully studied, will bring to anyone interested enough to devote a little time to it, a clear and definite mental conception of all color expression.

The author, Albert H. Munsell, was an artist of distinction, a gifted teacher, and, withal, a man of unusual scientific proclivities. The unassurance of the average artist's usual procedure led him early to wonder if guess work could not be supplanted by certainty. Investigations brought him immediately into the field of science. His practical knowledge as a painter, with its necessary training in close color observation, gave him a decided advantage over the scientist. Constant teaching produced the inevitable clearness of thought which aided in his investigations.

It was not long, however, before he realized that he must start from the beginning if a practical solution of the problem were to be developed. This involved quite revolutionary changes in his own previously acquired knowledge on the subject. The old red, yellow, blue theory would not answer. Visual mixture and pigment mixture did not always react similarly, and he realized that the eye produced color mixtures thousands of times daily as compared to the limited physical mixtures of pigments, confined to a few pigment users only. In starting from the beginning he was compelled to discover his own way out. It resulted first in the invention of the Munsell photometer for measuring value. This was followed by practical adaptations of Maxwell's disk spinning apparatus for Hue and Chroma measurements. Other devices and materials for simple experimental use and color study were invented and manufactured such as the color sphere, the color tree, the notation score cards, the Atlas of Color* and measured papers.

"A Color Notation" tells of many of these things, but even more than this it is a carefully worded description of the basis for all his work, an achievement that is gradually proving itself to be the only usable color presentation and notation which can be satisfactory in all cases. A casual reading fails to give the

* The present "Munsell Book of Color" is a revision and extension of the "Atlas of Color."

beginner a full comprehension of its scope and its completeness. Only by repeated study does one realize the magnitude of the task which Mr. Munsell so successfully set for himself and at the same time the thoroughness with which he compressed his ideas into this small volume. This ability to say in a few words well chosen and pointedly illustrative, what others might devote chapters to was a natural gift which made his teaching so effective.

In personal conversation and particularly in the classroom he would almost invariably tell some apt story or personal experience, which made his point, and left little to be added. The student found himself unconsciously applying the subtly given criticism with keen interest and deep concentration. Conviction follows such teaching. A really careful study of "A Color Notation" produces the same experience. The reader is convinced of the masterly handling of so complicated a subject and is left eventually with a deep conviction that Mr. Munsell has produced a clear, simple and altogether practical solution to the problem of color understanding, color visualization, color measurement, color balance, and color notation.

A general acceptance of Mr. Munsell's work as a basis for color development is rapidly bringing this field of expression into as current use and practice as music, for it is now as easily written and read as sound and with equal accuracy. The value of such use in education and industry can hardly be over-estimated.

In a discussion of Mr. Munsell's work some critics have stated that anything of this kind must cramp one's style; "limit the artist"; and "hamper free expression." Perhaps similar remarks were called forth by music critics before music notation was fully developed, yet one ventures to assert that the greatest master of music today feels liberated instead of bound down by his expert knowledge of the attributes of sound and its simple recording on the instrumental or vocal music score.

No doubt the reason for the early development of musical notation is due to the fact that sound is transient, and so cannot be captured in so permanent form as color. One is tempted to wonder whether music scores would be so common today if the phonographic music record had come first. Colors, on the other hand, may be fixed more or less permanently through dyes, pigments, glass, etc., and thus retained for matching and duplicating purposes. So the work of the visual color analysis and the abstract writing of colors was left undone. The world has gotten along; it might still continue to carry on, but modern industry, education, science, and art will, of practical necessity, come sooner or later, to a practice and analysis of color through some kind of color notation, which must have a basis built upon such work as Munsell has accomplished. Accurate recording of color is a growing necessity in business where it is rapidly increasing in scope and with varied applications. This alone is reason enough for a serious study of the measurement and notation of color. Beyond that a more universal knowledge and practice of the subject must bring untold benefit and pleasure to all who understand and, with intelligent assurance, use it. Albert H. Munsell has pioneered and given us the fundamental approach to this use.

ROYAL B. FARNUM
Former Director, Rhode Island School of Design

[9]

ILLUSTRATIONS

CONTENTS

CHAPTER I

COLOR NOTATION

CHAOS—Misnomers for Color

WRITING from Samoa on Oct. 8, 1892, to Sidney Colvin in London, Stevenson* says: "Perhaps in the same way it might amuse you to send us any pattern of wall paper that might strike you as cheap, pretty and suitable for a room in a hot and extremely bright climate. It should be borne in mind that our climate can be extremely dark, too. Our sitting room is to be in varnished wood. The room I have particularly in mind is a sort of bed and sitting room, pretty large, lit on three sides, and the colour in favor of its proprietor at present is a topazy yellow. But then with what colour to relieve it? For a little work-room of my own at the back, I should rather like to see some patterns of unglossy—well, I'll be hanged if I can describe this red—it's not Turkish and it's not Roman and it's not Indian, but it seems to partake of the two last, and yet it can't be either of them because it ought to be able to go with vermilion. Ah, what a tangled web we weave—anyway, with what brains you have left choose me and send some—many—patterns of this exact shade."

Where could be found a more delightful cry for some rational way to describe color? He wants "A topazy yellow" and a red that is not Turkish nor Roman nor Indian, but that "seems to partake of the two last, and yet it can't be either of them." As

* Page 194 "Vailima Letters," New York, Scribner's, 1901.

a cap to the climax comes his demand for "patterns of this exact shade." Thus one of the clearest and most forceful writers of English finds himself unable to describe the color he wants. And why? Simply because popular color terms convey different ideas to different persons.

When used inappropriately they invite mistakes and disappointments, for they do not clearly state a single one of the three qualities united in every color, which must be known to convey one person's color conceptions to another.

Music is equipped with a system by which it defines each sound in terms of its pitch, intensity, and duration, without allusions to the endless varying sounds of nature. So should color be supplied with an appropriate system.

It would, of course, be a waste of time to attempt the naming of every kind and degree of color, but there is a clue to this labyrinth if one will approach the problem with "a clear mind, a good eye, and a fair supply of patience."

ORDER—Visual qualities of Color

A child gathers flowers, hoards colored beads, chases butterflies and begs for the gaudiest painted toys. At first his strong color sensations are sufficiently described by the simple term of red, yellow, green, blue, and purple. But he soon sees that some are light, while others are dark, and later comes to perceive that each hue has many grayer degrees. Thus he early recognizes three ways in which colors differ.

Consciously or not, all skillful use of color must reckon with these simple but important facts.

Every color sensation unites three distinct qualities, defined as HUE, VALUE, and CHROMA. One quality may be varied without disturbing the other. Thus, a color may be weakened or strengthened in Chroma without changing its Value or Hue. Or its Hue may be modified without changing its Value or Chroma. Finally, its Value may be changed without affecting its Hue or Chroma.

A single term or name cannot define changes in this tri-dimensional balance which to the eye is a single color, as for instance, the difference between the two sides of a red cloth, one of which has been faded by exposure to the sun. Let us here define more explicitly the three terms which can describe these changes.

It may sound strange to say that color has three dimensions, but it is easily proved by the fact that each of them can be measured separately. Thus, in the case of the faded cloth; its redness or Hue, the amount of light or its Value, and its departure from gray of the same Value or its Chroma, can each be measured independently.

*Hue is the name of a Color**

It is that quality by which we distinguish one *color family from another,* as red from yellow, or green from blue or purple. It is specifically and technically that distinctive quality of coloring in an object or on a surface; the respect in which red, yellow, green, blue, and purple differ from one another; that quality in which colors of equal luminosity and chroma may differ. Science attributes this quality to difference in length of ether waves impinging on the retina, which causes the sensation of color.

Value is the lightness of a Color

It is that quality by which we distinguish a *light color from a dark one.* Color values are loosely called tints and shades, but these terms are frequently misapplied. A tint should be a light Value, and a shade a dark Value; but the word shade has become a general term for any type of color so that a shade of yellow may prove to be lighter than a tint of blue.

* Strictly speaking HUE is the family name for a group of chromatic colors.

A COLOR NOTATION

Chroma is the strength of a Color

It is that quality of color by which we distinguish a strong color from a weak one; the degree of departure of a color sensation from that of white or gray; the intensity of a distinctive Hue; color intensity.

The omission of one of these attributes leaves us in doubt as to the character of a color, just as surely as the character of a room would remain undefined if the length were omitted and we described it as 22 feet wide by 14 feet high. The imagination would be free to ascribe any length it chose. This length might be differently conceived by every individual who tried to supply the missing factor.

Much of the popular misunderstanding of color is caused by ignorance of those three dimensions or by an attempt to make two dimensions do the work of three. The chart and chips in the folder inserted herein will serve to illustrate the three dimensions or attributes of color known in the Munsell system as Hue, Value and Chroma.

SOLIDS—Graphic representation of Color order and relationship

To illustrate the tri-dimensional nature of colors it will aid the memory to visualize them upon our hand (Fig. 1). We may call the

Fig. 1

thumb of the left hand RED, the forefinger YELLOW, the middle finger GREEN, the ring finger BLUE, and the little finger PURPLE. When the finger tips are in a circle, they represent a circuit of hues, which has neither beginning nor end, for we can start with any finger and trace a sequence forward or backward. Now we enclose the tips together for white, and imagine that the five strong hues have slipped down to the knuckles. Still lower down at the wrist is black.

The hand thus becomes a color holder with white at the finger tips, black at the wrist, strong colors around the outside, and weaker colors within the hollow. Each finger is a scale of its own Hue, with white above and black below, while the graying of all Hues is traced by imaginary lines which meet in the middle of the hand.

Or again suppose we peel an orange, and divide it into five parts, leaving the sections slightly connected at the bottom. (Fig.

Fig. 2

2). Then let us say that all the reds we have ever seen are gathered in one of these sections, all the yellows in another, all the greens in a third, all the blues in a fourth and the purples in a fifth. Next, let us assort these colors, in each section, so that the lightest are at the top, and grade regularly to the darkest at the bottom.

The fruit is then filled with assorted colors, graded from white to black, according to their VALUES, and disposed of by their HUES in the five sections. A slice near the top will disclose light values of all hues, and a slice near the bottom will disclose dark values of the same hues. A slice across the middle shows a circuit of hues all of middle value; that is, midway between the extremes of black and white.

Two color dimensions are thus shown in the orange, and it remains to exhibit the third, which we have learned is Chroma. To do this, we have only to take each section in turn, and, without disturbing the values already assorted, shove the grayest in toward the narrow edge, and grade outward to the most intense at the surface. Each slice across the fruit still shows the circuit of the hues in one uniform value; but the strong chromas are at the outside while the weaker chromas make a graduation inward to neutral gray at the center where all trace of Hue disappears. The thin edges of all segments unite in a scale of neutrals from black to white, no matter what Hue each contains.

The curved outside of each section shows its particular Hue graded from dark to light values; and, should we cut the section at right angles to the thin edge, it would show the third dimension—Chroma—for the Hue is graded evenly from the surface to neutral gray.

Having used the familiar structure of the orange as a help in classifying colors, let us substitute a geometric solid, like a sphere

(Fig. 3), and make use of geographical terms. The north pole is white. The south pole is black. The equator is a circuit of middle reds, yellows, greens, blues, and purples. Parallels above the equator describe this circuit in lighter values, and parallels below trace it in darker values. The vertical axis joining black and

Fig. 3

white is a neutral scale of gray values, while perpendiculars to it are scales of Chroma. Thus, our color notions may be brought into orderly relation by the color sphere. Any color describes its color quality, light, and strength, by its place in the combined scales of Hue, Value, and Chroma.

Flat diagrams showing hues and values but omitting to define chromas, are as incomplete as would be a map of Switzerland with the mountains left out, or a harbor chart without indications of the depths of the water. We find by aid of the measuring instruments that coloring materials are very unequal in the third dimensions,—Chroma—producing mountains and valleys on the color sphere,* so that when the color system is worked out and

* Note: No regular solids portray the unequal degrees of value and chroma disclosed by measurement, but the *sphere* suggested by Runge (1810) is a convenient model for the establishment of balanced relations and locates all elements which combine to produce color harmony and color discord.

charted, some of the hues must be traced well out beyond the spherical surface. Indeed a COLOR TREE is needed to display, by unequal levels and lengths of its branches, the individuality of each hue. But, whatever solid figure is used to illustrate color relations, it must combine the three scales of Hue, Value, and Chroma, and these definite scales furnish a name for every color based upon its intrinsic qualities, and free from terms purloined in other sensations, or caught from the fluctuating colors of natural objects.

The COLOR TREE is made by taking the vertical axis of the sphere which carries a scale of Value, for the trunk (Fig. 4).

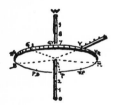

Fig. 4

The branches are at right angles to the trunk; and, as in the sphere, they carry the scale of Chroma. The branches are equi-distantly spaced around the trunk according to the Hue with each branch of colors placed at its correct value level. The yellow will appear nearest white at the top, and then green, red, blue, and purple branches; approaching the base of the trunk in the order of their values. It will be remembered that the Chroma of the sphere ceased at the surface, with the maximum of $/_5$ at the equator. The COLOR TREE prolongs this so that the branch ends represent the most powerful red, yellow, green, blue, and purple pigments which we now possess and could be lengthened should stronger chromas be discovered.

Such models set up a permanent image of color relations. Every point is self-described by its place in the united scales of Hue, Value, and Chroma. These scales fix each new perception of color in one's mind by its situation in the color solid. The importance of such a definite image can hardly be over-estimated, for without it one color sensation tends to efface another. When one looks at a color, and has no basis of comparison, it soon leaves a vague memory that cannot be described. These models, on the contrary, lead to an intelligent estimate of each color in terms of its Hue, its Value and its Chroma.

Thus defined, a color falls into logical relation with all other colors in the system, and is easily memorized, so that its image may be recalled at any distance of time or place by the notation.

NOTATION—*A systematic nomenclature*

The notation used in this system places Hue (expressed by an initial) at the left; Value (expressed by a number) above and to the right of the Hue symbol; and Chroma (also expressed by a number) below and to the right of the slanting line. Thus $R^5/_{10}$ means Hue (red), Value (^{5})/ Chroma /($_{10}$) and will be found to represent the qualities of the pigment vermilion.

HUE

Let a circle stand for the equator of the color sphere with the five principal hues (written by their initials R, Y, G, B, and P) spaced evenly about it. Some colors are neighbors, and unite to make a Hue which retains a suggestion of both. It is intermediate between two principal Hues. The intermediate between red and yellow is called Yellow-red, between green and yellow is called Green-yellow, between blue and green is called Blue-green, between purple and blue is called Purple-blue, between red and purple is called Red-purple, and they are written by their joined initials as YR, GY, BG, PB, and RP, respectively.

Each principal Hue has thus made two close neighbors by uniting with the nearest principal Hue on either side.

VALUE

We may designate the values on the neutral axis by writing them $N^0/$, $N^1/$, $N^2/$, $N^3/$, $N^4/$, $N^5/$, $N^6/$, $N^7/$, $N^8/$, $N^9/$, and $N^{10}/$, describing a regular scale from white at $N^{10}/$ to black at $N^0/$. Middle value ($N^5/$), as the name implies, stands midway between white and black. *When this numbered scale of values is familiar it serves not only to describe light and dark grays but the Value of chromatic colors which are at the same level in the scale.*

Middle colors are on a plane passing through the equator of the sphere—so that a middle red will be written $R^5/$, suggesting the steps 6, 7, 8, and 9, which are above the equator, and the steps 4, 3, 2, and 1, which are below.

Thus $R^5/$ is neither lighter nor darker than the gray of $N^5/$. A numeral written above to the right of the Hue symbol always indicates Value, whether of a neutral or a chromatic color, so that $R^1/$, $R^2/$, $R^3/$, $R^4/$, $R^5/$, $R^6/$, $R^7/$, $R^8/$, $R^9/$, describes a regular scale of red values, while $G^1/$, $G^2/$, $G^3/$, etc., is the scale of green values.

CHROMA

Chroma is the third and most subtle color quality. One is unconsciously familiar with the contrast between a strong red (vermilion) and a weak red (old brick). These are written $R^5/_{10}$ and $R^5/_2$. The chroma passes from grayish red through medium red out to the strongest red in the chroma scale obtained by vermilion.* The intervening steps of chroma are expressed by appropriate numerals. Thus $R/_1$, $R/_2$, $R/_8$, etc., is the scale of red chroma.

It is evident that still closer neighboring Hues exist between each consecutive pair in the circle of ten hues, that closer steps

* Note: Pigments and dyes have been developed since with a chroma far beyond $/^{10}$.

of Value exist between each consecutive pair on the value scale, and that closer steps of chroma exist between each consecutive pair on a Chroma scale, and if the process were continued long enough, the color steps would become so fine that the eye could see only a series of colors melting imperceptibly one into the other. Hence, this system includes orange, violet, etc., and gives them more appropriate names. It includes and arranges *all* color sensations on a measured foundation, even providing for still stronger colors, should science discover them. Such measures refute old blunders, and establish the true order of color as created by the eye.

COLOR CHARTS

Words are incomplete expression for color. Color scales are needed to train the visual estimate of color, and such scales cannot be left to personal whim or guess work. They should be standardized by scientific methods or they will fluctuate with each inspection and even vary from day to day according to the mental and physical poise of the individual.

To display these scales we must prepare cross sections or charts of the solid, some horizontal, some vertical, and some concentric with the neutral axis.

Such a set of charts form an atlas* of the color solid, enabling one to visualize and use any color in its relation to all other colors, and name it by its degree of Hue, Value, and Chroma.

Nor need we confine these charts to horizontal slices. Suppose we cut obliquely downward from the strongest yellow to the strongest purple-blue. This discloses a fascinating sequence which is the pigment echo of a prismatic spectrum, plus the purples which are lacking in the prism series.

* Note: For description of atlas see appendix A.

COLOR NOTATION

SUMMARY

The loose terms applied to color cause much misunderstanding. What one calls blue, another thinks of as purple-blue, or blue-green. The notion of typical red varies with almost every person examined. The common effort to define a "shade of red" by two qualities, ignoring the third and most subtle quality makes agreement well nigh impossible.

The Munsell System classifies color relations. The classification depends on the recognition of three color dimensions—VALUE, HUE, and CHROMA—arranged spatially as follows: A central vertical axis represents changes in value (painter term for luminosity) from black at the bottom to white at the top, the progression being logarithmic to follow the Weber-Fechner law.* The value of every point on this axis determines the level of every possible color of equal value. Vertical planes intersecting in this axis represent particular hues, the opposed portions being complementary in hue. Any three planes separated by 120° form a complementary trio, etc. Thus the angular position of any hue is determined. Chroma (intensity of hue or saturation) is measured by the perpendicular distance from any point to the vertical axis, its progress being arithmetical.

Thus is constructed a solid in which every horizontal plane corresponds to one and only one value; every radial plane contains colors of but one hue, and the surface of each cylinder concentric with the axis contains colors of equal chroma. Each point in this solid stands for one and only one color, and when these dimensions of a color have been measured, its position in the solid is obvious.

* Note:
Recent detailed experiments fix $N^3/$ as reflecting 6.56%; $N^5/$, 19.77%; $N^7/$, 43.06%

A COLOR NOTATION

The possibilities of this system are very great. It possesses elements of simplicity and attractiveness. It gives one almost unconsciously power of color discrimination. It provides not only a rational color nomenclature, but also a system of scientific importance, and of practical value.

COLOR ANARCHY IS REPLACED BY SYSTEMATIC COLOR DESCRIPTION.

CHAPTER II

COLOR SCORE

Fig. 5

PREVIOUS chapters describe hue, value, and chroma as well as their inter-relations in the color sphere and color tree. In addition we have seen how each color is *written* by a letter and two numerals, showing its place in the three scales of hue, value, and chroma. This naturally suggests, not only a record of each separate color sensation, but also a union of these records in series and groups to form a *color score,* similar to the musical score by which the measured relations of sound are recorded.

A very simple form of color score may be easily imagined as a transparent envelope wrapped around the equator of the sphere, and forming a vertical cylinder (Fig. 5). On the envelope the equator traces a horizontal center line, which is at 5 of the *value scale,* with zones 6, 7, 8, and 9 as parallels above, and the zones 4, 3, 2, and 1 below. Vertical lines are drawn through ten equidistant points on this center line, corresponding with the divisions of the *hue scale,* and marked R, YR, Y, GY, G, BG, B, PB, P, and RP.

The transparent envelope is thus divided into one hundred compartments, which provide for ten steps of value in each of the ten middle colors. Now, if we cut open this envelope along one of the verticals,—as, for instance, red-purple (RP), it may be spread out, making a flat chart of the color sphere (Fig. 6).

A COLOR NOTATION

A cylindrical envelope might be opened on any desired meridian, but it is an advantage to have green (G) at the center
of the chart, and it is there-
fore opened at the opposite
point, red-purple (RP). To
the right of the green center
are the meridians of green-
yellow (GY), yellow (Y),
yellow-red (YR), and red

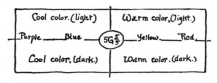

Fig. 6

(R), all of which are known as *warm colors,* because they contain yellow and red. To the left are the meridians of blue-green
(BG), blue (B), purple-blue (PB), and purple (P), all of which
are called *cool colors,* because they contain blue. Green, being
neither warm nor cold of itself, and becoming so only by addi-
tions of yellow or of blue, thus serves as a balancing point or
center in the hue-scale.*

The color score presents four large divisions or color fields
made by the intersection of the equator with the meridian of
green. Above the center are all light colors, and below it are
all dark colors. To the right of the center are all warm colors,
and to the left are all cool colors. Middle green ($5G^5/_5$) is the
center of balance for these contrasted qualities, recognized by all
practical color workers. The chart forms a rectangle whose
length equals the equator of the color sphere and its height equals
the axis (a proportion of 3.14:1), representing a union and balance of the scales of hue and of value. This provides for two
color dimensions; but, to be complete, the chart must provide
for the third dimension, chroma.

* To put this in terms of the spectrum wave lengths, long waves at the red end of
the spectrum give the sensation of warmth, while short waves at the violet end cause
the sensation of coolness. Midway between these extremes is the wave length of
green.

Replacing the chart around the sphere and joining its ends, so that it re-forms the transparent envelope, we may thrust a pin through at any point until it pierces the surface of the sphere. Indeed, the pin can be thrust deeper until it reaches the neutral axis, thus forming a scale of chroma for the color point where it enters. In the same way any colors on the sphere, within the sphere, or without it, can have pins thrust into the chart to mark their place, and the length by which each pin projects can be taken as a measure of chroma. If the chart is now unrolled, it retains the pins, which by their place describe the hue and value of a color, while their length describes its chroma.

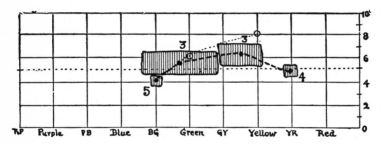

Fig. 7. COLOR SCORE—GIVING AREAS BY H, V, AND C

With this idea of the third color dimension incorporated in the score we can discard the pin, and record its length by a numeral. Any dot placed on the score marks a certain degree of hue and value, while a numeral beside it marks the degree of chroma which it carries, uniting with the hue and value of that point to give us a certain color. Glancing over a series of such color points, the eye easily grasps their individual character, and connects them into an intelligible series (Fig. 7).

Thus a flat chart becomes the projection of the color solid, and any color in that solid is tranferred to the surface of the chart, retaining its degrees of hue, value, and chroma. So far the scales have been spoken of as divided into ten steps, but they may be subdivided much finer, if desired, by use of the decimal point. It is a question of convenience whether to make a small score with only the large divisions, or a much larger score with a hundred times as many steps. In the latter case each hue has ten steps, the middle step of green being distinguished as $5G^5/_5$, to suggest the four steps 1G, 2G, 3G, 4G, which precede it, and 6G, 7G, 8G, and 9G, which follow it toward blue-green.

Such a color score, or notation diagram, to be made small or large as the case demands, offers a very convenient means for recording color combinations, when pigments are not at hand.

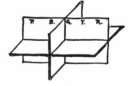

Fig. 8

* * *

To display its three dimensions, a little model can be made with three visiting cards, so placed as to present their mutual intersection at right angles (Fig. 8). $5G^5/_5$ is their center of mutual balance. A central plane separates all colors into two contrasted fields. To the right are all warm colors, to the left are all cool colors. Each of these fields is again divided by the plane of the equator into lighter colors above and darker colors below. These four color fields are again subdivided by a transverse plane through $5G^5/_5$ into strong colors in front and weak colors beyond or behind it.

Any color group, whose record must all be written to the right of the center, is warm, because red and yellow are dominant. One to the left of the center must be cool, because it is

COLOR SCORE

dominated by blue. A group written all above the center must have light in excess, while one written entirely below is dark to excess. Finally, a score written all in front of the center represents only strong chromas, while one written behind it contains only weak chromas. From this we gather that a balanced composition of color preserves some sort of equilibrium, uniting degrees of warm and cool, of light and dark, and of weak and strong, which is made at once apparent by the dots on the score.

* * *

A single color, like that of a violet, a rose, or a buttercup, appears as a dot on the score, with a numeral added for its chroma. A parti-colored flower, such as a nasturtium, is shown by two dots with their chromas, and a bunch of red and yellow flowers will give by their dots a color passage, or "silhouette," whose warmth and lightness is unmistakable.

The chroma of each flower written with the silhouette completes the record. The hues of a beautiful Persian rug, with dark red predominating, or a verdure tapestry, in which green is dominant, or a Japanese print, with blue dominant, will trace upon the score a pattern descriptive of its color qualities. These records, with practice, become as significant to the eye as the musical score. The general character of a color combination is apparent at a glance, while its degrees of chroma are readily joined to fill out the mental image.

When the plotting of color groups has become instinctive from long practice, it opens a wide field of color study. Take as an illustration the wings of butterflies or the many varieties of pansies. In the same way, rugs, tapestries, mosaics,—whatever attracts by its beauty and harmony of color,—can be recorded and studied in measured terms, and the mental process of estimating hues, values, and chromas, and areas by established scales must lead to finer perceptions.

The same process serves as well to record the most annoying and inharmonious groups, collecting them together with those groups which preserve such effects of color as are generally pleasing. When sufficient of these records have been obtained, they furnish definite material for a contrast of the color combinations which please, with those that cause disgust. Such a contrast should discover some broad law of color harmony. It will then be measured in terms which can be clearly given; not a vague series of personal contradictory statements conveying different meanings to each one who hears it, but rather a more reliable statement, impartially obtained.

CHAPTER III

COLOR ARRANGEMENTS

BALANCE—Visual comfort

NOW that we are supplied with a decimal scale of grays represented by divisions of the neutral axis (N^1/, N^2/, etc.) and a corresponding decimal scale of value for each of the ten hues ranged about the equator, traced by ten equidistant meridians from black to white, it is not difficult to foresee what the combination of any two colors will produce, whether they are at the equator already considered, or whether they are at different levels.

Let us think of the results of combining different values of opposite hues, as, for instance, YR^7/ and B^3/ (Fig. 9). To this

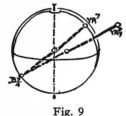

Fig. 9

combination the color sphere gives a ready answer; for the middle of a straight line through the sphere, and joining them, coincides with the neutral center, showing that they BALANCE ABOUT NEUTRAL GRAY. This is also true of any opposite pair of surface hues where the values are equally removed from the equator.

This raises the question, What is balance of Color? Artists criticize the color schemes of paintings as being "too light or too dark" (unbalanced in value), "too weak or too strong" (unbalanced in chroma), "too hot or too cold" (unbalanced in hue), showing that this is a fundamental idea underlying all color arrangements.

The simplest idea of balance is the equilibrium of two halves of a stick supported at its middle point. If one end is heavier than the other the support must be moved to that end.

But, since color unites three qualities, we must seek some type of triple balance. The game of jack straws illustrates this, when the disturbances of one piece involves the displacement of the others.

Triple balance may be graphically shown by three discs in contact. Two of them are suspended by their centers, while they  remain in touch with a third supported on a pivot, as in Fig. 10. Let us call the lowest disc HUE and the lateral discs VALUE and CHROMA. Any dip or rotation of the lower disc H will induce sympathetic action in the two lateral discs V and C. When H is inclined both V and C dip outward. If H is rotated, both V and C rotate, but in opposite directions. Indeed, any disturbance of V affects H and C, while H and V respond to any movement of C. So we must be prepared to realize that any change of one color quality involves readjustments of the other two.

Fig. 10

The sense of comfort is the outcome of balance, while marked unbalance immediately urges a corrective. That this approximate balance is desired may be shown by reference to our behavior, as to temperatures, quality of smoothness and roughness, degrees of light and dark, proportions of work and rest. One special application of this quality is balance which underlies beautiful color schemes. The use of strongest chromas only fatigues the eyes, which is also true of the weakest chromas. In a broad way we may say that color balances at neutral gray. Thus a moderate amount of extremely strong color may be balanced by a right amount of grayer color and a brilliant point of a strong red will balance a larger field of grayest blue-green. So we learn that *area* is another quality in color composition, which aids in the balance of hues, values, and chromas. Examples of this are all about us. The circus wagon and poster, although they yell successfully for our momentary attention soon become so painful to the vision that we turn from them. Other examples are magazine covers and billboards. These are all cases where color is used only to excite the eye but not for the purpose of permanent pleasure. In the case of the balanced color scheme, the problem is to soothe and please the eye so that the attention will remain upon it. Although the colors may differ greatly, their total effect is balance.*

Let us assume that the center of the sphere is the most simple natural balancing point for all colors, then colors equally removed from the center must balance one another. Thus white balances black. Lighter red balances darker blue-green. Middle red balances middle blue-green. In short, every straight line through the center indicates opposite qualities which balance one another. The color points so found are said to be "complementary," for each supplies what is needed to complement or balance the other in Hue, Value, and Chroma.

Let us now take a balance point upon the color sphere such as $R^5/_5$. Equal departures either way from this must balance, such as $R^7/$ with $R^3/$; $R^8/$ with $R^2/$; $R^6/$ with $R^4/$; while the

* One outstanding point, which may come as somewhat of a surprise to many of those chiefly interested in the practical application of color to advertising or to other fields in which color composition is an all important element, is that a careful study of Mr. Munsell's writings proves beyond the slighest trace of doubt that his ideas on "Balance" were far broader than often has been assumed. Mr. Munsell considered "Balance" about neutral gray, merely as the simplest and most elementary form of balance, which should be mastered by the thorough student of color before going on to the more interesting centers of balance (one mentioned being R^5/s) which forms the natural background in Mr. Munsell's mind for much of color harmony as presented later in this chapter. In the preceding chapter Mr. Munsell makes use of $5G^5/s$ as a center of balance.

strength may be used so as to require equal or unequal areas of each balanced pair.

The general law is, that *the stronger the color we wish to employ, the smaller must be its area, while the larger the area, the grayer or weaker the chroma.* Thus $R^7/_6$ balances $R^3/_8$ in the proportion of nine parts of the lighter red to forty-two parts of the darker red. In other words, these symbols will balance color *inversely* as the product of their factors. This opens up a great field of *area* in the use of reds, where balance may be restored by change of the factors of value and chroma. Thus the lighter red $(R^7/_6)$ which we will call "42," balances the darker red $(R^3/^3)$ which we will call "9," by giving 42 parts to the darker, weaker red, and 9 parts to lighter, stronger red.

Color balance soon leads to a study of optics in one direction, to aesthetics in another, and to mathematical proportions in a third, and any attempt at an easy solution of its problems is not likely to succeed. It is a very complicated question, whose closest counterpart is sought in musical rhythms. The fall of musical impulses upon the ear can make us gay or sad, and there are groups of colors which, acting upon the eye, can convey pleasure or pain to the mind.

That any long duration of unbalance, either mental, physical or spiritual is an aggravated form of disease, may be easily shown. Yet short periods of unbalance are very stimulating in the effort which they produce to regain balance. We see this in the introduction of discords in music. In contortions of the body. In intentional inversions of thought. This also shows in the seasoning of our food. Too sweet, too salt, too sour. It even shows in our criticisms of pictures. We say, too light, too dark, too hot, too cold, too weak, too strong, and the effort of the accomplished artist is to overcome these forms of unbalance.

COLOR ARRANGEMENTS

The introduction in a color scheme of a certain amount of unbalance is called harsh color, it leads to its correction by what we call harmonious color (really balanced); and the contrast enhances the latter; so that to overcome monotony, we should be able to use unbalance wisely at times, in order that the general balance may be the more evident. This is sometimes done in the picture galleries by means of a so-called "gallery of horrors": in music by a sudden discord: in behavior by an unexpected rudeness; all illustrations of the value of the contrast between harmony and discord: and this quality of contrast is proportioned to the use of color. If it serves as the background of the picture, the color must be quiet. If it is to be the make-up of the pictures themselves there must be strong oscillations in the contrast of Value, Hue, and Chroma. As in the case of advertising, especially in the open air, the very strongest contrasts and even strident relations are admissible.

A colorist is keenly alive to these feelings of satisfaction or annoyance, and consciously or unconsciously he rejects certain combinations of colors and accepts others. Successful pictures and decorative schemes are due to some sort of balance uniting "light and shade" (value), "warmth and coolness" (hue), with "brilliance and grayness" (chroma), for, when they fail to please, the mind at once begins to search for the unbalanced quality, and complains that the color is too hot, too dark, or too crude. This effort to establish pleasing proportions may be unconscious in one temperament, while it becomes a matter of definite analysis in another.

Any real progress in color education must come not from a blind imitation of past successes, but by a study into laws which they exemplify. To exactly copy fine Japanese prints or Persian rugs or Renaissance tapestries, while it cultivates an appreciation of their refinements, does not give one the power to create things equally beautiful. The masterpieces of music correctly rendered do not of a necessity make a composer. The musician, besides the study of masterpieces, absorbs the science of counterpoint, and records by an unmistakable notation the exact character of any new combination of musical intervals which he conceives.

Without a measured and systematic notation, attempts to describe color harmony only produce hazy generalities of little worth in describing our sensations, and fail to express the essential differences between "good" and "bad" color arrangement. So must the art of the colorist be furnished with a scientific basis and a clear form of color notation. This will record the successes and failures of the past, and aid in a search, by contrast and analysis, for the fundamentals of color balance.

COLOR HARMONY—Rhythmic Composition

Attempts to define the laws of harmonious color have not attained marked success, and the cause is not far to seek. The very sensations underlying these effects of concord or of discord are themselves undefined.

The term color harmony, from associations with musical harmony, presents to the mind an image of color arrangement,— varied, yet well proportioned, grouped in orderly fashion, and agreeable to the eye. Musical harmony explains itself in clear language. It is illustrated by fixed and definite sound intervals, whose measured relations form the basis of musical composition. The musical analogy gives us the clue, that a measured and orderly relation underlies the idea of harmony.

Instead of theorizing let us experiment. As a child at the piano who first strikes random and widely separated notes, but soon seeks for the intervals of a familiar air, so let us, after roaming over the color globe and its charts, select one color familiar to us, and study others that will combine with it to please the eye.

PATHS

Here is a grayish green stuff for a dress. What colors may be used with it? First let us find it on our sphere, so as to realize its relation to other degrees of color. Its value is $^6/$,—one step above the equator (middle value). Its hue is green, and its chroma $/_5$. It is written $G^6/_5$.

Color paths lead out from this point in every direction. Where shall we find harmonious colors, where discordant, where those paths more frequently traveled? Are there new ones still to be explored?

There are three typical paths: one vertical, with rapidly changing value; another lateral, with rapid change of hue; and a third inward, through the neutral center to seek the opposite field (Fig. 11).

The *vertical path* finds only lighter and darker values of gray-greens,—"self colors or shades," they are generally called,—and

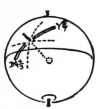

Fig. 11

offers a safe path, even for those deficient in color sensation, avoiding all complications of hue, and leaving the eye free to estimate different degrees of a single quality.

The *lateral path* passes through neighboring hues on either side. In this case it is a sequence from blue, through green into yellow. This is simply a change of hue, without change of value or chroma if the path be level, but, by inclining it, one end of the sequence becomes lighter, while the other darkens. It thus becomes an intermediate between the first and second typical paths, combining at each step a change of hue with a change of value. This is more complicated, but also more interesting, showing how the character of the gray-green dress will be set off by a lighter hat of Leghorn straw, and further improved by a trimming of darker blue-green. The sequence can be made still more subtle and attractive by choosing a straw whose yellow is stronger than the green of the dress, while a weaker chroma of blue-green is used in the trimming. This is clearly expressed by the notation thus: $Y^8/_7$, $G^6/_5$, $BG^4/_8$ (Fig. 11).

A sheet of paper large enough to hide the color sphere may be perforated with three or more openings in a straight line, and applied against the surface, so as to isolate the steps of any sequence which we wish to study. Thus the sequence given in the paragraph above—$Y^8/_7$, $G^6/_5$, $BG^4/_3$,—may be changed to bring it on the surface of the sphere, when it reads $Y^8/_3$, $G^6/_5$,$BG^4/_5$. A mask with round holes, spaced so as to uncover these three spots relieves the eye from the distraction of other colors. Keeping the center spot on green, the mask may be moved so as to study the changing hue or value of the other two steps in the sequence.

The *inward path* which leads to the neutral center, and on to the opposite hue of red-purple, $RP^4/_5$, is full of pitfalls for the inexpert. It combines great change of hue and chroma, with a small change of value.

If any other point be chosen in place of gray-green, the same typical paths are just as easily traceable, written by notation, and recorded on a score.

In the construction of the color solid we saw that its scales were made of equal steps in Hue, Value, and Chroma, and tested by balance on the center of neutral gray. Any steps will serve as a point of departure to trace regular sequences of the three types. The vertical type is a sequence of value only. It is somewhat tame, lacking the change of hue and chroma, but giving a monotonous harmony of regular values. The horizontal type traces a sequence of neighboring hues, less tame than the vertical type, but monotonous in value and chroma. The inward type connects opposite hues by a sequence of chroma balanced on middle gray and is more stimulating to the eyes.

Another very interesting path, which combines all three of the typical paths above, connects opposite hues by passing around the sphere instead of through it (Fig. 12). Let us illustrate this path by using as our key colors Yellow and Purple-blue. Such a path swinging from Y to PB passing through GY, G, BG, and B traces a sequence of hues, of which each step is less chromatic and darker than its predecessor.

This diminishing sequence is easily written thus: $Y^8/_7$, $GY^7/_6$, $G^6/_5$, $BG^5/_4$, $B^4/_3$, $PB^3/_2$. Its hue sequence is described by the

Fig. 12

initials: Y, GY, G, BG, B and PB. Its value sequence appears in the numerals above the line: 8, 7, 6, 5, 4, and 3, while the chroma sequence is included in the lower numerals 7, 6, 5, 4, 3, and 2. This gives a complete statement of the sequence defining its peculiarity, that at each change of hue there is a regular change of value and chroma.

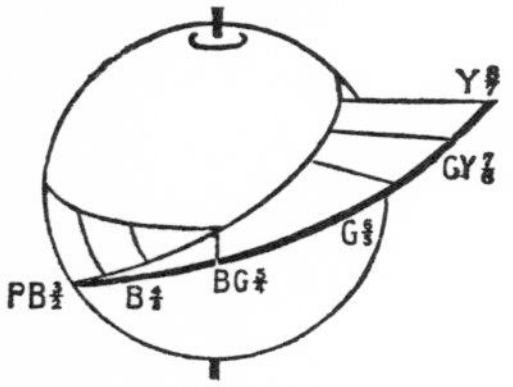

Nature seems to be partial to this sequence, constantly reiterating it in yellow flowers with their darker green leaves and underlying blue shadows. In the spring she may narrow its range making the blue more green and the yellow less red, but in the Autumn she seems to widen the range, presenting strong contrasts of YR and PB.

Every day she plays upon the values of this sequence. From the contrasts of light and shadow at noon to the hardly perceptible differences at twilight. The chroma of this sequence expands during the summer to strong colors and contracts during the winter to grays. Indeed, Nature, who rarely repeats herself, yet is endlessly balancing inequalities of hue, value, and chroma by compensation of quantity, would seem to be the source of our notation of color harmony.

AREAS

As we have learned, small bits of powerful color can be used to balance large fields of weak chroma. For instance, a spot of strong reddish purple is balanced and enhanced by a field of gray-green.

So an amethyst pin at the neck of the girl's dress will appear to advantage with the gown, and also with the Leghorn straw. But a large field of strong color, such as a cloth jacket of reddish purple would be fatal to the measured harmony we seek.

This use of a small point of strong chroma, if repeated at intervals, sets up a notion of rhythm; but, in order to be rhythmic, there must be recurrent emphasis, "a succession of similar units combining unlike elements." This quality must not be confused with the unaccented succession, seen in a measured scale of Hue, Value, or Chroma.

Change of interval immediately modifies the character of a color sequence. The variations of color sequences are almost endless; yet upon a measured system the character of each effect is easily described, and if need be, preserved by a written record.

COLOR ARRANGEMENTS

Experiments with variable masks for the selection of color intervals soon stimulate the imagination, so that it conceives sequences through any part of the color solid. The color image becomes a permanent mental adjunct. Five middle colors, tempered with white and black, permit us to devise the greatest variety of sequences, some light, some dark, some combining small differences of chroma with small intervals of hue, and so on through a well-nigh inexhaustible series.

As this constructive imagination gains power, the solid may be laid aside. We can think of color consecutively. Each color suggests its place in the system, and may be taken as a point of departure for the invention of groups to carry out the desired relationship.

APPENDIX A

THIS system has grown out of the experiences of the artist and teacher rather than those in the laboratory. Yet, the perception of color relations involving Physiology, Psychology, and Physics, makes it necessary at each important step to consult these sciences.

PHYSIOLOGY

Back of the eye lies that function which discriminates various color sensations and proceeds to act upon them. This color judgment is swayed by several factors and is liable to deception.

Freshness or fatigue of the nervous system tells powerfully upon color decisions, and even momentary fatigue of the retina may play us unwelcome tricks. It may cause delusions, as in the case of the mother who glanced up from work upon a piece of vivid scarlet cloth, and shrieked at the look on her baby's face, believing its apparent pallor meant death. The rosy complexion of the baby had not changed in the slightest degree, but her fatigued eyes could see no red for the moment, giving only a ghastly mixture of the two remaining sensations, green and blue. Had the cloth reflected a vivid blue-green, she might have been equally overwhelmed by a contrary illusion that the child was feverish.

This retinal fatigue is far reaching in its effects. Its skillful employment brings about extraordinary results, as in the paintings of Monet, Sisley, Pissarro, and other impressionists.

APPENDIX A

Contrast is another subtle element of coloristic art. The simplest form appears when two colors in contact seem different from what they would when viewed separately. Their interval seems to be increased because the lighter of the two appears more luminous, while the darker appears still more dark than it is. Each becomes tinged with the complement of the other, which may enhance or degrade it, according to what colors are chosen.

Consciously or not, all skillful use of color has to reckon with these very important factors.

PSYCHOLOGY

Perception of color is crude at first. The child sees only the most obvious distinctions, and prefers the strongest stimulation. Many children find it difficult to express more than five steps of the chroma scale, while easily making ten steps of value and from twenty to thirty-five steps of hue. This interesting feature is of psychologic value. But perception soon becomes refined by exercise. With this gain in perception he finds a strong desire to invent arrangements to please his fancy.

The condition of normal balance is the source of this visual contentment. Whatever stimuli we use, the eye demands approximate balance and resents unbalance in proportion to the effort it makes to regain equilibrium. Color arrangements, which preserve it, we call harmonious. Annoy the eye by disturbing this balance and we exclaim "how ugly." This explains our aversion to the gaudy billboard, which assaults the retina with a chromatic shriek.

PHYSICS—A Prismatic color solid

The solar spectrum and the rainbow are the most stimulating color experiences with which we are acquainted. With a little effort of the imagination we can picture a prismatic color sphere, using only the colors of light. In a cylindrical chamber is hung a *diaphanous* ball similar to a huge soap bubble, which can display color on its surface without obscuring its interior. Then, at the proper points of the surrounding wall, three pure beams of colored light are admitted,—one red, another green, and the third violet-blue.

They fall at proper levels on three sides of the sphere, while their intermediate gradations encircle the sphere with a complete spectrum plus the needed purple. As they penetrate the sphere, they unite to balance each other in neutrality. Pure whiteness is at the top, and, by some imaginary means their light gradually diminishes until they disappear in darkness below.

The lightest part of the spectrum is a narrow field of greenish yellow, grading into darker red on one side and into darker green on the other, followed by still darker blue and purple-blue. Upon the sphere the values of these spectral colors trace a path high up on the yellow section, near white, and slanting downward across the red and green sections, which are traversed near the level of the equator, it goes on to cross the blue and purple well down toward black.

This forms an inclined circuit, crossing the equator at opposite points, and suggests the ecliptic or the rings of Saturn. A pale rainbow would describe a slanting circuit nearer white, and a dimmer one would fall within the sphere, while an intensely brilliant spectrum projects far beyond the surface of the sphere, so greatly is the chroma of its hues in excess of the common coloring materials with which we work out our problems.

It is well to recognize the place of the spectrum in this system, not only because it is the established basis of scientific study, but especially because the invariable order assumed by its hues is the only stable hint which Nature affords us in her infinite color play.

COLOR EDUCATION

The teacher's skill is shown in searching out the simplest and most easily grasped facts; in finding not only an "easy door" but the "right door"; in leading the children through the maze of color by steps so clearly understood and remembered that he will safely find his way along and not become confused.

We do not train the ear to discriminate musical sounds with the idea that each student will produce artistic results. That is only for a few chosen natures in special advanced schools. But a simple discipline in tone discrimination is good for all, and a simple training in color qualities is equally the right of every student.

An examination of school programs shows that the aim of color study ranges from a simple discipline of the judgement and memory, through exercises of a decorative character, to attempt at picturesque composition, and even the analysis of the masterpieces of color. This last is a very ambitious aim.

Let us concentrate public education upon a simple and definite training of the eye, so that it may be quick to recognize, define, imitate and memorize the colors in daily use.

The same broad principles which govern the presentation of other ideas apply with equal force in this study. A little, well apprehended, is better than a mass of undigested facts. If one is led to discover, or at least to think he is discovering, new things about color, the mind will be kept alert and seek out novel illustrations at every step. Now and then a pupil will be found who leads both teacher and class by intuitive appreciation of color, and it is a subtle question how far such a nature can be helped or hindered by formal exercises. But such an exception is rare, and goes to prove that systematic discipline of color sense is necessary for most people.

A tri-dimensional perception, like our sense of color, requires skillful training, and each lesson must be simplified to the last point practicable. It must not be too long, and should lead to some definite results which a student can grasp and express with some tolerable accuracy, while its difficulties should be approached by easy steps, so as to avoid failure or discouragement.

Vocational color work includes much more than the atmospheric values by which an artist imitates natural effects, and the broad field of industrial color work is largely so conventional that it retains no hint of representation. A training in definite scales and color sequences, where the pupil clearly understands his problem and may recognize just the degree by which his efforts fall short of success, will develop finer and finer discriminations.

Outdoor nature and indoor surroundings offer endless color illustrations. Birds, flowers, minerals, and other objects in daily use take on a new interest when their varied colors are brought into a conscious relation, and clearly named.

THE CHROMATIC TUNING FORK

Beauty of color lies in *tempered* relations. Music rarely touches the extreme range of sound, and harmonious color arrangements rarely use the extremes of color-light or color-strength. Regular scales in the middle register are first given to train the ear, and so should the eye be first familiarized with medium degrees of color.

Exact imitation and memorizing of the middle scale on the piano is now universally adopted as an introduction to a study of music. Similarly the five middle hues, measured and balanced, form a simple introduction to the study of harmonious color composition.

APPENDIX A

The Munsell System provides measured scales, established by special instruments, and is able to select the middle points of red, yellow, green, blue, and purple as a basis for comparing and relating all. These FIVE MIDDLE COLORS, equal in chroma and equal in value, so that they differ only in hue, may aptly be called a *tuning fork of color,* for they are the starting point in judging equal departures to the extremes of white and black, and to the extremes of no color (*i. e.* neutrality) and strong colors (*i. e.* maximum chroma). What makes it still more valuable is that these middle colors largely predominate in successful work, so that if these five are in one's hand when he visits the art museum he will find them and their near neighbors used in beautiful rugs, tapestries, enamels, and paintings, while the maxima of red, yellow, blue, will be conspicuous by their absence. If any traces appear they will be as small accents of strong color opposed to a large field of quiet and balancing chroma.

So that for both theoretical and practical reasons these tempered colors should be first recognized, imitated and impressed upon the memory, as a means for rightly estimating the unequal chromas of the maxima.

COLOR ATLAS

In 1915 Mr. Munsell published "The Atlas of the Munsell Color System," a series of charts showing visual scales of Hue, Value, and Chroma. This was the first step in establishing the visual degree of latitude and longitude, as well as the elevation of all points within the color solid. In 1929 "The Atlas of the Munsell Color System" was superseded by the Munsell "Book of Color." This later book is patterned after the constant hue charts of the original Atlas and contains extensions of all the scales, made possible by the more recent development of stronger permanent pigments.

A COLOR NOTATION

Since 1929 the Book of Color has been revised and extended several times. It is now available in both mat and glossy finish, the most extensive edition containing over 1,200 dfferent colors. The charts in the Book of Color represent vertical half-sections through Munsell color space, with each chart showing a series of colors all of the same Munsell hue, but varying in value and chroma. The complete series includes 40 of the constant hue charts.

To understand how the Book of Color is made and used, let us imagine we have a great collection of various colors of silks or cottons or papers, which we wish to classify, and have at hand a convenient filing cabinet. Its ten drawers are numbered from one at the bottom to ten at the top. Such samples as appear very dark shall go in the bottom drawers. Those visually halfway between white and black shall be placed in the middle or fifth drawer, and so on, until all the colored samples are arranged in the proper levels.

The middle drawer contains many hues, all of middle value, and with varying amounts of chroma. The hues may be placed in a circuit ranging from red, through its many gradations to yellow, then to green, blue, purple and back to red. Within each hue the samples are graded in a radial line from the center of this circuit, with the grayest colors nearest the center and the more saturated colors (higher chromas) toward the outer edge.

This middle drawer would then represent a horizontal section through color space or, in Munsell terms, a constant value chart. When the upper (lighter) drawers and lower (darker) drawers are similarly arranged they would produce constant value charts at lighter and darker values. If a vertical rod is pushed down through the center of this cabinet it traces a scale of neutral grays from white at the top to black at the bottom.

APPENDIX A

We have thus constructed a three dimensional color solid, with each color placed in its proper position in relation to other colors. To display this color solid in two dimensions it is necessary to divide it into sections in such a manner that one of the Munsell attributes of hue, value and chroma is constant while the other two are variable.

As indicated above, a horizontal section through the color solid produces a constant value chart, with the appropriate neutral color in the center. From this center radiate lines of constant hue. On each of these constant hue lines the colors become increasingly more saturated as they depart from neutral. Cylindrical sections centered around the neutral pole and extending to various radial distances from it, when flattened out, represent constant chroma charts. Thus a chart made from the $/_4$ chroma section would include all colors of that chroma, with hue varying along the horizontal dimension and value varying along the vertical dimension.

A vertical slice through the neutral pole would display two complementary hues separated by a neutral value scale. Such a chart, when cut in half at the neutral pole, yields two charts. Each chart has colors of a single hue, with value increasing from bottom to top and chroma increasing from neutral out toward the most saturated colors available for that hue and value level. This is called a constant hue chart. The Munsell Book of Color displays 40 of these constant hue charts containing colors of the 40 hues for which standard papers representing the notation are available.

EVALUATION

THE ideal system for color should be fundamentally simple and logical in its structure. It should be based on such definite truth that every element incorporated may find expression in practice. This is a day when mere theories will not suffice. They must be sifted in the determination to find only that which has a practical application in answering the desires and needs of man. The system devised by Albert H. Munsell has proved itself to be both simple and practical. Out of a chaos of conflicting fictions and truths Mr. Munsell was able to assemble the fundamentals of color thought and put them in order in such a logical manner that we are impressed, as we are with all great things, with the utter simplicity of this order.

With the beginning of the present century the concept of color presented in this book was indeed new to all but a few physicists. Now most books and articles on color speak freely about the three attributes, hue, value, and chroma, as if they always had been common property. The idea of measure applied to color astonished the world, especially the art world. Measure as applied to music or to architecture was accepted, but the realism that a foot-rule also might be applied, analytically and creatively, to color composition had only begun to grow and was not yet entirely established. Since then decorative and expressive art, more noticeably in the commercial field, has steadily increased its demand and its appreciation for measured color. The realm of modern packaging has been revolutionized through its use.

APPENDIX A

It was not until Munsell demonstrated the visual properties of color with his simplicity that we were able to see the relation between the Maxwell discs of the physicists and the resultant tonality of the artist's composition. Yellow and Purple-blue paints may produce a green resultant on the palette, but yellow and Purple-blue areas placed in a color composition produce no optical sensation of greenness. With this distinction clear as we turn to Munsell in this present book we find a whole world of visual color possibilities floating before us. The gates to a new art of color are set ajar in Mr. Munsell's suggestions of color harmony and schematic arrangements based on measured degrees of hue, value, and chroma. Out of the vague dawn of feeling comes the clear day of understanding. Feeling plus understanding has such possibilities!

MILTON E. BOND
Instructor of Design and Color

A great many people have the idea that the Munsell system and the "Book of Color" are Mr. A. H. Munsell's primary contributions to color. I do not believe that this is so. His contribution lies in a much more fundamental matter. A notation for color was upon his mind, and "A Color Notation" was the result. This revised book makes this all very clear, and will make it easy to go back to his own words for a description of what he had in mind. The Atlas (or Book of Color), the photometer, the color wheel, or any other aids, were merely a means of making the Munsell color notation useful.

DOROTHY NICKERSON
Color Technologist

TRADITIONAL COLOR NAMES

A STUDY of over 2,000 named colors which have been collected from sample cards and various other sources, leads to the conclusion that color names may be divided into two general classes. Certain color names, such as "pink," "brown," "orange," etc., have a traditional association with fairly definite areas or ranges of colors. On the other hand, many other color names are of more recent origin and have not been used with the necessary definiteness for a sufficient length of time to warrant classifying them as traditional color names.

The student of color in his own work should, if possible, avoid the use of traditional color names, because they apply to *areas* of color rather than to specific colors. It is only by recognizing and using the three dimensions of color that he can accurately comprehend and describe the difference between any two colors, and especially between any two "pinks," "browns," etc. However in describing color to those who have not had the opportunity of studying the simple method of color notation described in this book, it is sometimes helpful to know the correlation between this exact color notation and traditional color names.

For this reason, twenty-four of the most common names are summarized on the following pages. Each name, of course, represents a group of colors, the limits of which have been more or less clearly defined by usage. The approximate extent of each group is given directly under the Group Name. Thus the term "Pink" (see group No. 1) is applied to a range of colors extending from about Red-purple to Red Yellow-red in HUE, all of which colors are *light* in VALUE and *moderate* in CHROMA.

The survey, upon which this work is based, brought out the interesting fact that certain portions of the areas covered by many of the twenty-four color groups might be occupied by colors bearing closely related color names. For instance, "Garnet," "Bordeaux," "Claret Red," and "Wine Red" were found to lie within the MAROON Group. Such color names are listed alphabetically, with an appropriate cross reference to group headings.

ALPHABETICAL LIST OF NAMES
with their Group Numbers

NAME	GROUP	NAME	GROUP
Amber	7	Chalk White	24
Apple Green	11	Chestnut	7
Auburn	7	Chocolate	7
		Claret Red	3
Baby Blue	14	Coal Black	22
Battleship Gray	23	Cocoa	7
Black	22	Cream	8
Black, Coal	22	Emerald Green	12
Blue, Baby	14	Garnet	3
Gendarme	16	Gendarme Blue	16
Light	14	Golden Brown	7
Midnight	16	Golden Yellow	9
National	15	Gray	23
Navy	16	Battleship	23
Royal	15	Iron	23
Sailor	16	Pearl	23
Sky	14	Smoke	23
Turquoise	13	Steel	23
Bordeaux	3	Green	11, 12
Briar Rose	2	Apple	11
Brown	7	Emerald	12
Golden	7	Nile	11
Seal	7	Gunmetal	23
Buff	6, 8		

A COLOR NOTATION
ALPHABETICAL LIST OF NAMES

NAME	GROUP	NAME	GROUP
Hazel	7	Plum	19
		Prune	19
Iron Gray	23		
Ivory	8	Red, Claret	3
Old	8	Red, Wine	3
		Rose	2
Jade	12	Briar	2
		Old	2
Lavender	18	Wild	2
Lead	23	Royal Blue	15
Lemon Yellow	9	Russet	7
Light Blue	14		
Light Pink	1	Sailor Blue	16
Lilac	18	Sand	6
		Scarlet	4
Magenta	21	Seal Brown	7
Maroon	3	Silver	23
Mauve	18	Sky Blue	14
Midnight Blue	16	Slate	23
		Smoke Gray	23
National Blue	15	Snow White	24
Navy	16	Steel Gray	23
Navy Blue	16	Straw	8
Nile Green	11		
		Tan	6
Old Ivory	8	Taupe	23
Olive	10	Tobacco	7
Olive Drab	10	Turquoise Blue	13
Orange	5	Violet	17
Orchid	20	White	24
		Chalk	24
Pale Pink	1	Snow	24
Pearl Gray	23	Wild Rose	2
Pink	1	Wine Red	3
Light	1	Yellow, Golden	9
Pale	1	Yellow, Lemon	9

APPENDIX B
COLOR GROUPS

Group No.	Traditional Color Name	Designation According to the Munsell System of Color Notation		
		HUE Limits	VALUE Limits	CHROMA Limits
1	PINK Light Pink Pale Pink	RP-R (4RP—8R)	Light (6.5/—8/)	Weak to Moderate (/1—/7.5)
2	ROSE Briar Rose Old Rose Wild Rose	R (8RP—7R)	Middle (3/—6/)	Moderate (/4—/7)
3	MAROON Bordeaux Claret Red Garnet Wine Red	R (9RP—6R)	Dark (2/—3/)	Moderate (/2—/6)
4	SCARLET	R (3R—7R)	Middle (3/—5/)	Very Strong (/12—/18)
5	ORANGE	YR (10R—6YR)	Middle (5.5/—7/)	Strong (/10—/14)
6	TAN Buff Sand	YR (3YR—10YR)	Middle to Light (4.5/—6.5/)	Weak to Moderate (/1—/4.5)
7	BROWN Amber Auburn Chestnut Chocolate Cocoa Golden Brown Hazel Russet Seal Brown Tobacco	YR (10R—10YR)	Dark to Middle (1.8/—5.5/)	Weak to Moderate (/1—/6)
8	IVORY Buff Old Ivory Straw	Y (1Y—5Y)	Light (7/—9/)	Weak (/1—/4)

Group No.	Traditional Color Name	Designation According to the Munsell System of Color Notation		
		HUE Limits	VALUE Limits	CHROMA Limits
9	LEMON YELLOW Golden Yellow	Y (3Y—7Y)	Light (6.5/—8.5/)	Strong (/7—/12)
10	OLIVE Olive Drab	Y-GY (4Y—10Y)	Dark to Middle (2.5/—4.5/)	Weak to Moderate (/2—/4)
11	NILE GREEN Apple Green	GY (5GY—10GY)	Light (7/—8.5/)	Weak to Moderate (/3—/6)
12	EMERALD GREEN Jade	G (10GY—5G)	Dark to Middle (2.5/—5/)	Strong (/7—/10)
13	TURQUOISE BLUE Turquoise	BG-B (5BG—2B)	Middle to Light (5/—6.5/)	Moderate (/3—/6)
14	SKY BLUE Baby Blue Light Blue	B (1B—8B)	Light (6.5/—8.5/)	Weak to Moderate (/1—/6)
15	ROYAL BLUE National Blue	PB (4PB—7PB)	Dark (2/—3.5/)	Strong (/8—/14)
16	NAVY BLUE Gendarme Midnight Blue Navy Sailor Blue	PB (4PB—10PB)	Dark (2/—3.5/)	Weak to Moderate (/1—/5)
17	VIOLET	P (9PB—5P)	Dark (2.5/—4.5/)	Moderate to Strong (/5—/10)
18	LAVENDAR Lilac Mauve	P (2P—7P)	Middle to Light (4.5/—7/)	Weak to Moderate (/3—/8)
19	PLUM Prune	P-RP (5P—5RP)	Dark (2/—3.5/)	Weak to Moderate (/2—/5)
20	ORCHID	P-RP (5P—2RP)	Middle to Light (4.5/—7/)	Weak to Moderate (/3—/8)

APPENDIX B

COLOR GROUPS

Group No.	Traditional Color Name	Designation According to the Munsell System of Color Notation		
		HUE Limits	VALUE Limits	CHROMA Limits
21	MAGENTA	RP (2RP—7RP)	Dark (2.5/—3.5/)	Moderate to Strong (/6—/12)
22	BLACK Coal Black	—	Very Dark (0/—3/)	None to Very Weak (/0—/1)
23	GRAY Battleship Gray Gunmetal Iron Gray Lead Pearl Gray Silver Slate Smoke Gray Steel Gray Taupe	— Neutral to slight departure in any Hue.	Dark to Light (3/—8/)	None to Very Weak (/0—/1)
24	WHITE		Very Light (8/—10/)	None to Very Weak (/0—/1)

GLOSSARY OF COLOR TERMS

ABSOLUTE BLACK: A color of the lowest VALUE. It possesses neither HUE nor CHROMA. It is closely approximated when looking through a small aperture into a velvet-lined box. *See* Black.

ABSOLUTE WHITE: A color of the very highest VALUE. It possesses neither HUE nor CHROMA. It is closely approximated by viewing a piece of freshly-cleaned block of magnesia. *See* White.

ACHROMATIC COLORS: *See* Neutral Colors.

ATTRIBUTES of Color: *See* Color Dimensions.

BLACK: A Neutral Color of very low VALUE, usually about one and one-half in VALUE. *See* Absolute Black. *See* also Table of Traditional Color Names.

CHROMA: *The strength or weakness of a Chromatic Color.* In terms of CHROMA, color is described as *Weak, Moderate,* or *Strong.* Synonyms: Saturation; Intensity (Purity). *See* Chromatic Colors.

CHROMATIC COLORS*: Includes all colors other than Neutral

* Note: When the meaning is perfectly clear, we can and do use the word Color in the sense of Chromatic Color. Terms such as Color Blindness, Color Photography, or Color Printing intrinsically are perfectly understandable. It is only in a technical treatise that one should use the terms Chromatic Color Blindness, Chromatic Color Photography, Chromatic Color Printing, etc.

Colors. (*See* Neutral Colors) They are characterized by the p r e s e n c e of both HUE and CHROMA. *See* also Color.

COLOR: *Anything seen by the eye,* such as Black, White, Red, Yellow, Green, Blue, or Purple. The form of an object is recognized only because of the contrast between the color or colors of this object and the color or colors of the background. Color is accompanied by an excitation of the retina and brain by beams of light. *See Chromatic* Colors; Neutral Colors.

COLOR BALANCE: 1. *In its beoadest meaning, color balance is an aesthetic term referring to the feeling of balance, continuity, and fitness which is found in beautiful color schemes.*

2. In a more restricted sense, it applies to the physical balance of a color scheme in Gray. In such a case the colors in a c o l o r scheme are assembled on a disc in pie-shaped areas or sectors. The size of each of these sectors is proportional to the area of each color in the color scheme. If the disc areas blend to a Neutral Gray when the disc is rotated, the color scheme is said to balance. With experience this form of physical Color Balance can be detected solely by the eye. Studies and exercises in Color Balance will broaden one's experience and improve one's color

APPENDIX B

COLOR BALANCE—*Continued*
technique just as studies and exercises in Musical H a r m o n y broaden one's experience and improve one's musical technique. It is not suggested that studies and exercises be limited to Color Balance, since such studies are but the stepping stones leading to the study of Color Dominance. *See* Color Dominance.

COLOR BLINDNESS. The inability to distinguish colors properly which is associated with an abnormal perception of HUE and CHROMA. It may be either congenital or due to injury to the eye.

COLOR CHART: A series of Color Scales (*See* Color Scale), so arranged that any two dimensions of color vary in a regular manner, while the third dimension remains constant. *See* Color Dimensions.

COLOR DESCRIPTION: The delineation of color by means of words. A vocabulary of but fourteen words is sufficient for a simple description of any color. HUE is comprehended by five words—*Red, Yellow, Green, Blue,* and *Purple*—used either singly or in conjunction with each other. (*See* Major Hues.) The terms, *Black, Gray,* and *White* are used when HUE and CHROMA are absent. VALUE is comprehended by three words—*dark, middle,* and *light.* CHROMA is comprehended by three words—*weak, moderate,* and *strong.* The words describing VALUE may well be placed first, the HUE second, and the CHROMA third, as "a *Dark Red* of *moderate* CHROMA," *i.e.,* a Maroon.

C O L O R DIMENSIONS: HUE, VALUE, and CHROMA. These three dimensions describe any color as accurately and as readily as the three dimensions of a box describes its length, breadth and thickness. Synonyms: Color Attributes; Color Qualities. *See* Color.

COLOR DOMINANCE: This is found in a color scheme in which some one HUE predominates. Intelligently employed, it suggests different moods or atmospheres, typified in various cases by Valor, Inspiration, Fruitfulness, Truth, Royalty, etc.

There is no better training for the effective handling of Color Dominance than the study of Color Balance. *See* Color Balance.

COLOR NOTATION: An exact and specific description of a color, using symbols and numerals, written HUE/VALUE/CHROMA. For example, a typical Maroon is notated as "5R3/4." *See* Hue, Value, Chroma for notations of each. *See* also Color Description.

COLOR SCALE: A s e r i e s of colors, exhibiting a r e g u l a r change or gradation in one dimension, while the other two dimensions are constant. For instance, a VALUE Scale progresses by even-graded steps from Black to White. (*See* Value Scale.) A CHROMA Scale progresses by even-graded steps from Neutral Gray to a strong color. (*See* Chroma). A HUE Circle is a Scale of evenly-spaced Hues. (*See Hue* Circle.) *See* also Color Dimensions.

A COLOR NOTATION

COLOR SPHERE: *See* Index.

COLOR TREE: *See* Index.

COMPLEMENTARY H U E S : Two HUES which differ most radically from each other.

COOL C O L O R S : Blue-Green, B l u e, and Purple-Blue. *See* Warm Colors.

DARK COLOR: A color of low VALUE, found in or adjacent to the lower third of the VALUE Scale. *See* Value.

GRAY: 1. A color which possesses neither HUE nor CHROMA, i. e., a Neutral Color. (*See* N e u t r a l Color.) Where considerable clarity is desired, this meaning of Gray may be expressed as Neutral Gray. 2. Traditionally, Grays are colors between Black and White, possessing from zero to about one step of CHROMA. *See* Traditional Color Names.

HOME VALUE LEVEL: The VALUE level at which the maximum CHROMA is reached in some particular HUE. It varies for different HUES, i.e., in Yellow, it is at the eighth level; in Green, at the fifth level; and in Purple-Blue at the third level. The "home" level also varies for different color mediums. *See* Maximum Color.

HUE: *The distinctive character-istic* of any *Chromatic Color* distinguishing it from other hues, such as are found in the spectrum or between the ends of the spectrum. In terms of HUE we describe a color as *Red, Yellow,*

Green, Blue, or Purple. See also Chromatic Colors.

HUE CIRCLE: Exhibits a progressively-graded series of HUES, equally spaced to the eye, and of constant VALUE and CHROMA. *See* Hue Circuit.

HUE CIRCUIT: Exhibits a progressively-graded series of HUES; VALUE and CHROMA are not necessarily constant. *See* Hue Circle.

HUES: *See* Principal Hues; Intermediate Hues; Major Hues; Second Intermediate Hues; Special Intermediate Hues. *See* also Complementary Hues.

INTERMEDIATE HUES: Yellow-Red, Green-Yellow, Blue-Green, Purple-Blue, and Red-Purple. These five HUES are placed at the visually determined mid-points between the five Principal HUES.

HUE	Symbol	Notation
Yellow-Red	YR	5YR
Green-Yellow	GY	5GY
Blue-Green	BG	5BG
Purple-Blue	PB	5PB
Red-Purple	RP	5RP

See Principal Hues. *See* also Hue; Major Hues.

LIGHT: 1. Relates to nerve currents, set up in the optic nerve and brain by the stimulation of the retina due to the visible portion of the radiant energy thrown out by such a source as the sun. 2. The luminous energy which gives rise to color. 3. Energy times visibility.

APPENDIX B

LIGHT COLOR: A color of high VALUE, found in or adjacent to the upper third of the VALUE Scale. *See* Value.

LIGHT PRIMARIES: Three spectrally pure beams of light, by the blending of which a great number of colors can be seen. Three wave-lengths frequently used are 650 mμ, 550 mμ, and 460 mμ, corresponding in general to the hues RP-R, GY-G, and PB-P. *See* Primary Colors.

MAJOR HUES: Ten HUES, made up of the five Principal HUES and the five Intermediate HUES. (*See* Principal H U E S ; Intermediate HUES.) These ten HUES have been chosen not because they are ten in number—although the Decimal System is very convenient—but because they represent *mutually equidistant Hue-points to the eye. See* also Hue.

MAXIMUM COLOR: A color of very strong CHROMA, on a *value* level characteristic of the HUE in question—i. e., its "Home" VALUE level. (*See* Home Value Level.) As a general rule Maximum Yellow is on the **eighth** level of VALUE, Maximum Purple-Blue on the third level, etc. The reason for this interesting variation of Maxima Colors in different HUES is due not to any physical characteristics or complexities inherent in the colored media which we use, but rather to the sensitive and unique adjustment of the mechanism of the eye and brain.

The word HUE "Maximum" is a relative term, referring to the strongest color in any HUE which

can be evoked by some particular color medium. Thus the Maximum Color in any single HUE may vary for different color media. The maxima shown on the Munsell charts, which have been selected as the strongest colors which are reasonably permanent, represent one class of Maxima; printing inks represent another class of Maxima; and Oil Colors, Dyes, Ceramics, etc., further classes of Maxima.

MIDDLE COLOR: A color of middle VALUE, found in or adjacent to the middle third of the VALUE scale. The word "middle" should be differentiated from the word "moderate" as given in the next definition.

MODERATE COLOR: A color of moderate CHROMA, found near the fourth to sixth step of CHROMA on the Munsell Color Charts.

NEUTRAL COLORS: Characterized by a complete absence of HUE and CHROMA. They are pure Black, pure White, in addition to the pure Grays lying between. Synonym: Achromatic Colors. *See* Color; Chromatic Colors.

PIGMENT-MIXTURE PRIMARIES: A Red pigment, a Yellow pigment, and a Purple-Blue pigment. It is assumed that there are three pigments or three dyes, by the intermixture of which a considerable number of colors can be evoked. In practice there are more than three. For instance, two different pigments of the same HUE will act quite differently when mixed with a pigment of some other HUE. Such

PIGMENT-MIXTURE PRIMARIES—*Continued*

complexities are due to the multiple absorption of light within the pigment layer, and to the different sizes of the pigment granules.

Pigment-mixture Primaries describe the results of Pigment-mixture and as such are important. They are, however, positively misleading if one attempts to use them to describe color as the eye sees it.

PRIMARY COLORS.: These are assumed to be inherently more essential than certain other colors which result from the mixing or blending of the Primary Colors. There are three kinds of Primary Colors: Light Primaries, Pigment-mixture Primaries, and Psychological Primaries.

PRINCIPAL HUES: Red, Yellow, Green, Blue, and Purple. These five HUES have been chosen not because they are five in number, but because they are *visually equidistant from each other in Hue.*

HUE	Symbol	Notation
Red	R	5 R
Yellow	Y	5 Y
Green	G	5 G
Blue	B	5 B
Purple	P	5 P

See Intermediate Hues; Major Hues; Hue.

PSYCHOLOGICAL PRIMARIES: Black and White; Yellow and Purple-Blue; Red and Green. Dr. Christine Ladd-Franklin has proposed the very reasonable hypothesis that the simplest eye sees merely achromatic colors (*See* Achromatic Colors); that a more complex eye sees Yellow and Purple-Blue in addition to achromatic colors; and that in fully developed vision the ability to see Yellow splits up into the ability to see Red and Green. Her theory explains in this way how it happens that Red and Green, instead of making a series of reddish Greens (as Red and Purple Blue make a series of reddish Blues or Purples), vanish when mixed in proper proportion, and produce Yellow; and that in the same way, Yellow and Purple - Blue produce White. *See* Primary Colors.

REFLECTION FACTOR: The percentage of incident light reflected from a sample. *See* Value.

SECOND INTERMEDIATE HUES: Additional HUES placed at the visually determined midpoints between each of the ten Major HUES.

HUE	Symbol	Notation
Red Yellow-Red	R-YR	10 R
Yellow-Red Yellow	YR-Y	10 YR
Yellow Green-Yellow	Y-GY	10 Y
Green-Yellow Green	GY-G	10 GY
Green Blue-Green	G-BG	10 G
Blue-Green Blue	BG-B	10 BG
Blue Purple-Blue	B-PB	10 B
Purple-Blue Purple	PB-P	10 PB
Purple Red-Purple	P-RP	10 P
Red-Purple Red	RP-R	10 RP

See Major Hues; Hue.

SHADE: 1. The color evoked when looking at the mixture of a chromatic pigment with a black pigment or of a chromatic dye with a black dye. 2. The appearance of that portion of a surface which lies in a shadow. *See* Tint.

APPENDIX B

SPECIAL INTERMEDIATE HUES: All HUES not classified as Principal, Intermediate, or Second Intermediate HUES. The following list of HUES in the Red group shows the relation of the Special Intermediate HUES to the Major HUES and to the Second Intermediate HUES. *See* Hues.

Nota- tion	Classifica- tion	HUE
10 RP	{SECOND {INTERMEDIATE	} Red-Purple } Red
1 R	Special Intermediate	
2 R	Special Intermediate	
3 R	Special Intermediate	
4 R	Special Intermediate	
5 R	MAJOR	Red
6 R	Special Intermediate	
7 R	Special Intermediate	
8 R	Special Intermediate	
9 R	Special Intermediate	
10 R	{SECOND {INTERMEDIATE	} Red } Yellow-Red

SPECTRALLY PURE COLOR: *The sensation evoked from spectrally pure light* (i. e., from but a few closely-adjacent wave-lengths in the spectrum). *See* Visible Spectrum.

STRONG COLOR: A color of pronounced CHROMA, found in the neighborhood of the seventh to tenth steps of CHROMA. Colors of still stronger CHROMA may be described as *very strong*. *See* Chroma.

TINT: 1. The color evoked when looking at the mixture of a chromatic pigment and a white pigment. 2. The color evoked when small amounts of a pigment or dye are applied to a white paper or white cloth s u r f a c e. *See* Shade.

VALUE: *The lightness or darknes of any color.* In terms of VALUE we describe all colors as *dark, middle, or light.* There are no universally accepted synonyms for VALUE. Among those used to a limited extent are: Brightness; Brilliance; Luminosity.

VALUE LEVEL: A horizontal slice through the Color Solid on which all colors are of the same VALUE. *See* Color Sphere; Color Tree.

VALUE SCALE: A series of visually equidistant Neutral Colors, lying between Absolute Black and Absolute White. The revised Munsell VALUE Scale represents the averaged results obtained by seven experienced observers. The following table shows the relationship between VALUE and Reflection Factor. *See* Journal Optical Soc. of America, vol. 33, No. 7, page 406, July, 1943.

VISIBLE SPECTRUM: the result of passing a beam of light through a glass prism. By this means it is broken up into an invariable sequence of increasing wave-lengths of light, evident to the eye as a sequence of colors of subtly varying HUE and of very strong CHROMA. *See* Light.

WARM COLORS: Red, Yellow-Red, and Yellow. *See* Cool Colors.

WEAK COLOR: A color of reduced CHROMA, found in the neighborhood of the second or third steps of C H R O M A. *See* Chroma.

WHITE: A Neutral Color of very high VALUE, usually in the neighborhood of the ninth VALUE Level. *See* Absolute White. *See* also Traditional Color Names.

TABLE OF LUMINOUS
REFLECTANCES FOR MUNSELL VALUES*

Munsell Value	Percent Luminous Reflectance	Munsell Value	Percent Luminous Reflectance	Munsell Value	Percent Luminous Reflectance	Munsell Value	Percent Luminous Reflectance
0.0	.000						
.1	.120	2.6	4.964	5.1	20.68	7.6	52.30
.2	.237	2.7	5.332	5.2	21.62	7.7	53.94
.3	.352	2.8	5.720	5.3	22.58	7.8	55.63
.4	.467	2.9	6.128	5.4	23.57	7.9	57.35
.5	.581	3.0	6.555	5.5	24.58	8.0	59.10
.6	.699			5.6	25.62		
.7	.819	3.1	7.002	5.7	26.69	8.1	60.88
.8	.943	3.2	7.471	5.8	27.78	8.2	62.71
.9	1.074	3.3	7.960	5.9	28.90	8.3	64.57
1.0	1.210	3.4	8.471	6.0	30.05	8.4	66.46
		3.5	9.003			8.5	68.40
1.1	1.353	3.6	9.557	6.1	31.23	8.6	70.37
1.2	1.505	3.7	10.134	6.2	32.43	8.7	72.38
1.3	1.667	3.8	10.734	6.3	33.66	8.8	74.44
1.4	1.838	3.9	11.355	6.4	34.92	8.9	76.53
1.5	2.021	4.0	12.001	6.5	36.20	9.0	78.66
1.6	2.216			6.6	37.52		
1.7	2.422	4.1	12.66	6.7	38.86	9.1	80.84
1.8	2.642	4.2	13.35	6.8	40.23	9.2	83.07
1.9	2.877	4.3	14.07	6.9	41.63	9.3	85.33
2.0	3.126	4.4	14.81	7.0	43.06	9.4	87.65
		4.5	15.57			9.5	90.01
2.1	3.391	4.6	16.37	7.1	44.52	9.6	92.42
2.2	3.671	4.7	17.18	7.2	46.02	9.7	94.88
2.3	3.968	4.8	18.02	7.3	47.54	9.8	97.39
2.4	4.282	4.9	18.88	7.4	49.09	9.9	99.95
2.5	4.614	5.0	19.77	7.5	50.68	10.0	102.57

*This table supersedes similar ones for Munsell values published prior to 1943.

APPLICATIONS AND ADVANTAGES OF
THE MUNSELL SYSTEM

It is impossible to list in detail all the practical applications of this measured color system. However, the advantages of such a system of color classification may be summed up as follows:

1. Loose and unrelated color terms are replaced by a definite notation.

2. New colors in no way disturb the orderly classification, as a place is already awaiting them.

3. Each color names itself by its degree of hue, value, and chroma.

4. Colors may be easily and rapidly specified by direct perceptual comparison.

5. Each color can be recorded and transmitted by a simple code.

6. Color contracts can be drawn and proved by psychophysical tests.

7. Color tolerances can be readily and meaningfully expressed.

8. Color grading of many agricultural and industrial products can be readily accomplished.

9. Fading can be defined and plotted at certain intervals, showing its progress in quantitative terms.

10. Specifications may be re-expressed in terms of the C.I.E. or any related system.

INDEX

INDEX PAGE BY NUMBERS

MUNSELL HUE VALUE / CHROMA CHART
with
envelope of loose color chips

A SIMPLE illustration of the three attributes of color—hue, value and chroma—is achieved by pasting the loose color chips on the background chart printed on the inside of this folder.

A more extensive display of colors is provided in the ten major hues of the *Munsell Student Chart* collection and a far more extensive display is provided on the forty hue charts of the *Munsell Book of Color.*

A copy of the Munsell brochure-catalog, covering a description of the complete Munsell notation, categories of application, related color standards and technical services, will be furnished upon request.

MUNSELL COLOR

MACBETH DIVISION

OF KOLLMORGEN CORPORATION

2441 N. Calvert Street

Baltimore, Maryland 21218

KEY TO ORDERLY ARRANGEMENT OF COLORS

The following steps will assist in the proper arrangement on the chart of the 24 Munsell chips enclosed in the coin envelope:

A. Separate the chips into three groups.

    1. Chips of strong chroma (10).
    Red*, Yellow-Red, Yellow, Green-Yellow, Green, Blue-Green, Blue, Purple-Blue, Purple, Red-Purple.

    2. Chips which are neutral—no hue or no chroma (8). Black, Grays, White.

    3. Chips which are red or of reddish cast (6). Grayish red through strong red.

B. Arrange the 10 strong chroma chips on the positions indicated in the hue circle.
    Red (5R)*, Yellow-Red (5YR), Yellow (5Y), Green-Yellow (5GY) etc.

C. Arrange the 8 neutral chips on the left hand vertical scale. Darkest (N 2/) one up from bottom—with gradual increasing value to lightest (N 9/) at top.

D. Arrange the 6 grayish red to strong red chips on the horizontal scale at the 4/ value level.
    Weakest (most gray, 5R 4/2) at left, through increasing chroma (saturation) to strong red (5R 4/12) at right.

---

*The sample of strong red for the hue circle is of *lighter value* than the sample of strong red for the chroma scale.

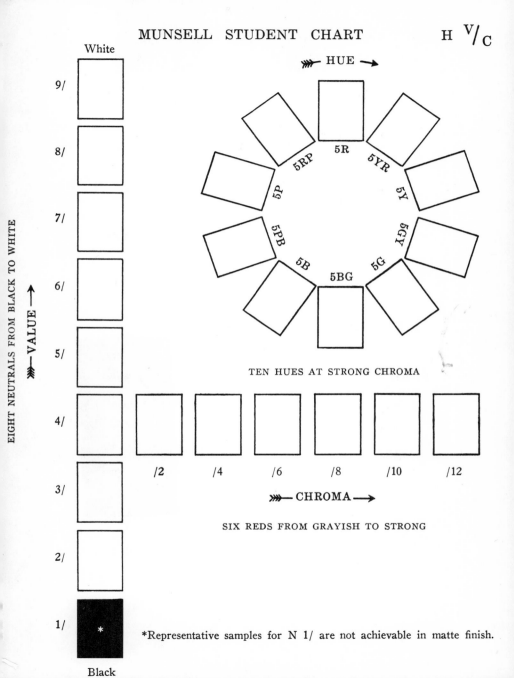

MUNSELL STUDENT CHART

H $^V/_C$

White

HUE

5RP 5R 5YR

5P 5Y

5PB 5GY

5B 5G

5BG

TEN HUES AT STRONG CHROMA

EIGHT NEUTRALS FROM BLACK TO WHITE

VALUE

9/

8/

7/

6/

5/

4/

3/

2/

1/ *

Black

/2 /4 /6 /8 /10 /12

CHROMA

SIX REDS FROM GRAYISH TO STRONG

*Representative samples for N 1/ are not achievable in matte finish.